101 favourite songs and melodies
101 beliebte Songs und Melodien
101 chansons et mélodies à succès

# MINI FAKE BOOK FOR

Arranged by Sally Adams

# TRUMPET

FABER *ff* MUSIC

ISBN 0-571-52688-8
EAN 978-0-571-52688-8

© 2008 by Faber Music Ltd
First published in 2008 by Faber Music Ltd
3 Queen Square London WC1N 3AU

Cover by Lydia Merrills-Ashcroft
Music processed by Jackie Leigh

Printed in England by Caligraving Ltd
All rights reserved

To buy Faber Music publications or to find out about the full range of titles available please contact your local retailer or Faber Music sales enquiries:

Faber Music Limited, Burnt Mill,
Elizabeth Way, Harlow CM20 2HX England
Tel: +44 (0) 1279 82 89 82
Fax: +44 (0) 1279 82 89 83
sales@fabermusic.com  fabermusic.com

£9.99

GW00391776

# CONTENTS

# FOREWORD

Before you begin playing the pieces in this book, prepare them carefully. Here's a good way to start work on each piece:

1. Think about the key and then play the scale (or the micro-scale, which is just the first five notes).
2. Then make sure you really understand the rhythm: clap the rhythm while tapping the pulse with your foot, for example.
3. Then explore the piece's 'ingredients' – articulation (e.g. staccato and accents) and dynamic markings. Play the scale again adding some of these markings or perhaps make up your own short piece that uses these same ingredients.
4. Finally think about the character or mood. How will you really bring the piece to life and convey its personality?

Above all enjoy your performances and always play with real musicianship and energy!

A NOTE ON CHORD SYMBOLS
Chord symbols have been included here in the key of the instrument. However, a separate PDF of chord symbols at concert pitch (for piano accompanying purposes) can be downloaded from fabermusic.com.

# (MEET) THE FLINTSTONES

Words and Music by Joseph Barbera,
William Hanna and Hoyt Curtin

# WHEN A KNIGHT WON HIS SPURS

Trad.

© 2008 by Faber Music Ltd

# THEME FROM SYMPHONY No.1

Johannes Brahms

# I TAUT I TAW A PUDDY-TAT

Words and Music by Billy May,
Warren Foster and Alan Livingston

# AGINCOURT SONG

Anon.

# LITTLE DONKEY

Words and Music by
Eric Boswell

# SLANE

Trad. Irish

# TRULY SCRUMPTIOUS
## (FROM *CHITTY CHITTY BANG BANG*)

Words and Music by
Richard Sherman and Robert Sherman

# PROMENADE
## (FROM *PICTURES AT AN EXHIBITION*)

Modest Musorgsky

# AUSTRIAN HYMN

Joseph Haydn

# BIMBLING ALONG

Sally Adams

# BEAUTIFUL DREAMER

Stephen Foster

# SOMEBODY LOVES ME
## (FROM *GEORGE WHITE'S SCANDALS OF 1924*)

Words by Buddy De Sylva and Ballard MacDonald
Music by George Gershwin

# HYFRYDOL

R. H. Prichard

# THE HIPPOPOTAMUS

Words by Michael Flanders
Music by Donald Swann

# THE ROSE OF TRALEE

Charles W. Glover

# SUNRISE, SUNSET
## (FROM *FIDDLER ON THE ROOF* )

Words by Sheldon Harnick
Music by Jerry Bock

# THE COONEY TUNE BLUES
## (*for Joseph Cooney*)

Sally Adams

# CABARET
## (FROM *CABARET*)

Words by Fred Ebb
Music by John Kander

# CHITTY CHITTY BANG BANG
## (FROM *CHITTY CHITTY BANG BANG*)

Words and Music by
Richard Sherman and Robert Sherman

# DON'T FENCE ME IN
## (FROM *HOLLYWOOD CANTEEN*)

Words and Music by
Cole Porter

# MENUET

George Frideric Handel

# THE BARE NECESSITIES
## (FROM *THE JUNGLE BOOK*)

Words and Music by
Terry Gilkyson

# FROSTY THE SNOWMAN

Words and Music by
Steve Nelson and Jack Rollins

# MAYPOLE DANCE

Paul Harris

# LET'S CALL THE WHOLE THING OFF
## (FROM *SHALL WE DANCE?*)

Words and Music by
George Gershwin and Ira Gershwin

# DANSE DES MIRLITONS
## (FROM *THE NUTCRACKER*)

Pyotr Ilyich Tchaikovsky

# WHEN YOU WISH UPON A STAR
## (FROM *PINOCCHIO*)

Words by Ned Washington
Music by Leigh Harline

# SOLDIERS' MARCH
## (FROM *ALBUM FOR THE YOUNG*)

Robert Schumann

# COME YE SONS OF ART

Henry Purcell

# CAN'T GET YOU OUT OF MY HEAD

Words and Music by
Cathy Dennis and Robert Davis

# JERUSALEM

Charles Hubert Hastings Parry

# A SPOONFUL OF SUGAR
## (FROM *MARY POPPINS*)

Words and Music by
Richard Sherman and Robert Sherman

# MAKE ME SMILE (COME UP AND SEE ME)

Words and Music by
Steve Harley

# RULE BRITANNIA!

Thomas Augustine Arne

# LIKE A PRAYER

Words and Music by
Madonna and Pat Leonard

# PLAISIR D'AMOUR

Johann Paul Martini

# TOP CAT

Words and Music by William Hanna,
Joseph Barbera and Hoyt Curtin

# BOURBONS

Sally Adams

# IF I WERE A RICH MAN
## (FROM *FIDDLER ON THE ROOF* )

Words by Sheldon Harnick
Music by Jerry Bock

# ROCKIN' ROBIN

Words and Music by
Jimmie Thomas

# BLOW, BLOW, THOU WINTER WIND

Thomas Augustine Arne

# ZIP-A-DEE-DOO-DAH
## (FROM *SONG OF THE SOUTH* )

Words by Ray Gilbert
Music by Allie Wrubel

# FLY ME TO THE MOON (IN OTHER WORDS)

Words and Music by
Bart Howard

# MORNING MISTS

Paul Harris

# PAVANE

Gabriel Fauré

# GET ME TO THE CHURCH ON TIME
## (FROM *MY FAIR LADY*)

Words by Alan Jay Lerner
Music by Frederick Loewe

# TOMORROW
## (FROM *ANNIE*)

Words by Martin Charnin
Music by Charles Strouse

# ANDANTE
## (FROM THE VIOLIN CONCERTO)

Felix Mendelssohn

# ETUDE Op.10 No.3

Frédéric Chopin

# (SITTIN' ON) THE DOCK OF THE BAY

Words and Music by
Otis Redding and Steve Cropper

# A WHITER SHADE OF PALE

Words and Music by
Keith Reid and Gary Brooker

# BYRNES HORNPIPE

Trad.

# PIE JESU
## (FROM THE REQUIEM )

Gabriel Fauré

# THE PRINCE OF DENMARK'S MARCH

Jeremiah Clarke

# (IS THIS THE WAY TO) AMARILLO?

Words and Music by
Neil Sedaka and Howard Greenfield

# VOIS-TU LA NEIGE QUI BRILLE?

Jean-Baptiste Arban

© 2008 by Faber Music Ltd

# AVE VERUM CORPUS

Wolfgang Amadeus Mozart

© 2008 by Faber Music Ltd

# KILLING ME SOFTLY WITH HIS SONG

Words by Norman Gimbel
Music by Charles Fox

# HEDWIG'S THEME
## (FROM *HARRY POTTER AND THE PHILOSOPHER'S STONE*)

Music by John Williams

# THE FLOWERS THAT BLOOM IN THE SPRING
## (FROM *THE MIKADO*)

W. S. Gilbert & Arthur Sullivan

# LULLABY OF BROADWAY

Words by Al Dubin
Music by Harry Warren

# WHO WANTS TO BE A MILLIONAIRE?
## (FROM *HIGH SOCIETY*)

Words and Music by
Cole Porter

# LA DONNA È MOBILE
## (FROM *RIGOLETTO*)

Giuseppe Verdi

# YOU'RE BEAUTIFUL

Words and Music by James Blunt,
Sacha Skarbek and Amanda Ghost

# THE CAN-CAN
## (FROM *ORPHEUS IN THE UNDERWORLD*)

Jacques Offenbach

# MARCH

George Frideric Handel

# ANYTHING GOES
## (FROM *ANYTHING GOES*)

Words and Music by
Cole Porter

# THEME
## (FROM *SWAN LAKE*)

Pyotr Ilyich Tchaikovsky

# SPRING SONG

Felix Mendelssohn

# SOMEONE TO WATCH OVER ME
## (FROM *OH, KAY!*)

Words and Music by
George Gershwin and Ira Gershwin

# AVE MARIA

Franz Schubert

# ELITE SYNCOPATION

Scott Joplin

# DIXIE

Daniel Emmett

# MISS OTIS REGRETS (SHE'S UNABLE TO LUNCH TODAY)
## (FROM *HI DIDDLE DIDDLE*)

Words and Music by
Cole Porter

# WAKE ME UP BEFORE YOU GO-GO

Words and Music by
George Michael

# POLOVTSIAN DANCE
## (FROM *PRINCE IGOR*)

Alexander Borodin

# TICO TICO

Zequinha Abreu

# BACK FOR GOOD

Words and Music by
Gary Barlow

# WINTER
## (FROM *THE SEASONS*)

Antonio Vivaldi

# TIPSY TANGO

Paul Harris

# SUMMER NIGHTS
## (FROM *GREASE*)

Words and Music by
Jim Jacobs and Warren Casey

# THE MAN WITH THE CHILD IN HIS EYES

Words and Music by
Kate Bush

# SONG OF INDIA
## (FROM *SADKO*)

Nicholas Rimsky-Korsakoff

# ANGELS

Words and Music by
Robert Williams and Guy Chambers

# WOULDN'T IT BE LOVERLY?
## (FROM *MY FAIR LADY*)

Words by Alan Jay Lerner
Music by Frederick Loewe

# IN THE HALL OF THE MOUNTAIN KING
## (FROM *PEER GYNT*)

Edvard Grieg

# I'M A BELIEVER

Words and Music by
Neil Diamond

# THEME FROM THE *NEW WORLD* SYMPHONY

Antonin Dvořák

# TRÄUMEREI

Robert Schumann

# WE GO TOGETHER
## (FROM *GREASE*)

Words and Music by
Jim Jacobs and Warren Casey

# THE SWAN
## (FROM *THE CARNIVAL OF THE ANIMALS*)

Camille Saint-Saëns

# DANCING QUEEN

Words and Music by Stig Anderson,
Benny Andersson and Björn Ulvaeus

# ROAD TO NOWHERE

Words and Music by
David Byrne

# ABI'S ARIA

Sally Adams

# THEME FROM PIANO CONCERTO No.21

Wolfgang Amadeus Mozart

# THEME FROM *WILLIAM TELL* OVERTURE

Gioacchino Rossini

# IF YOU'RE ANXIOUS FOR TO SHINE
## (FROM *PATIENCE*)

W. S. Gilbert & Arthur Sullivan

# AIR ON THE G STRING
## (FROM SUITE No.3)

Johann Sebastian Bach

# THIS TOWN AIN'T BIG ENOUGH
# FOR BOTH OF US

Words and Music by
Ronald Mael

# GRAND FANTASIA

Paul Harris